NEIL A. KJOS
PIANO LIBRARY

MW01014917

LEVEL ONE
Sight Reading

Piano Music for Sight Reading and Short Study

By Diane Hidy

ISBN-10: 0-8497-9848-5
ISBN-13: 978-0-8497-9848-1

Sight Reading (Preparatory Level through Level Ten) contains piano music of various textures and styles which may be used as a supplement to any course of study to improve sight reading, as well as overall reading skills.

"Sight reading" means playing music you have never seen before. In other words, reading music "at first sight." A good sight reader can play accurate notes, rhythms, dynamics and articulations at, or near, the given tempo. **The best way to become a good sight reader is to read new music every day**.

Here are some tips to help you progress:

Before you sight read, look through the entire piece and observe the:
- Time Signature
- Key Signature
- Clefs
- Dynamics
- Accidentals
- Slurs, Ties, Staccatos, Accents, etc.
- Rhythmic and Melodic Patterns

As you sight read:
1. Play at a slow to moderate tempo.
   - Use a metronome to help you keep a steady beat.
   - Count aloud as you play.
2. Keep your eyes on the music.
   - Avoid looking up and down from the music to your hands.
   - Look ahead in your music to see what is next.
3. Keep going, even if you make mistakes; avoid going back to fix anything.

After you sight read:
1. Evaluate your playing.
   - Were the notes and rhythms correct?
   - Were the dynamics and articulations markings clear and distinct?
   - Did the music continue to move forward as it maintained a steady beat?
2. Sight read the music again.
   - Concentrate on correcting any previous mistakes.
   - Set a goal for a perfect performance by the third reading. After playing a piece three times, you have begun to learn it, and are no longer sight reading.

Short Study pieces are meant to be practiced, but only for a few days or at most few weeks. These are not designed for polishing to performance level, but instead to help you improve your ability to learn new music quickly and efficiently.

"Short study" is about the *amount of time* you spend on a piece (for example, 5 minutes a day for one week), whereas "sight reading" is about the *number of times* you play a piece (no more than three).

If you can play the pieces in this book perfectly:
- *the first time through*, you might need to go to the book at the next higher level to improve your sight reading.
- *the third time through*, you are at the right level for improving your sight reading.
- *after a few days of practice*, you are in the right level for short study music.

1.

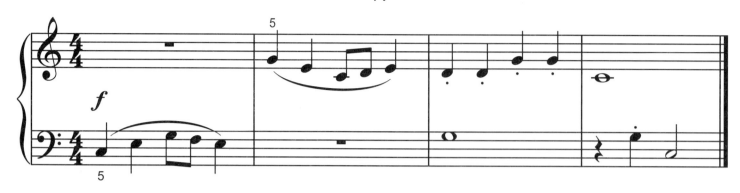

2.

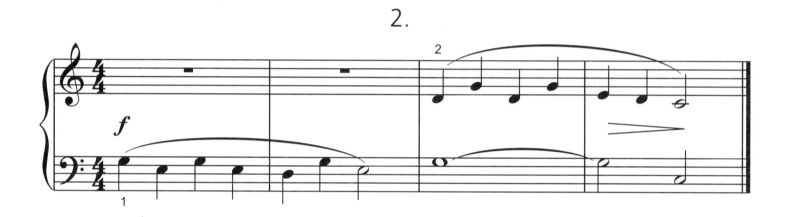

3.

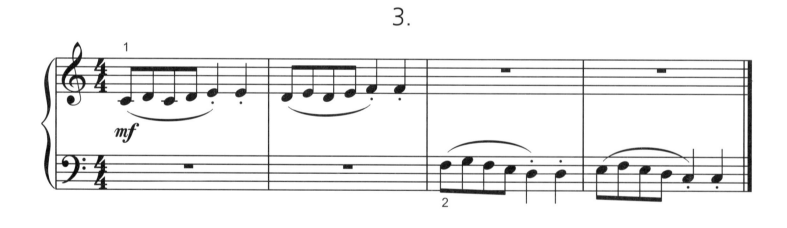

4.

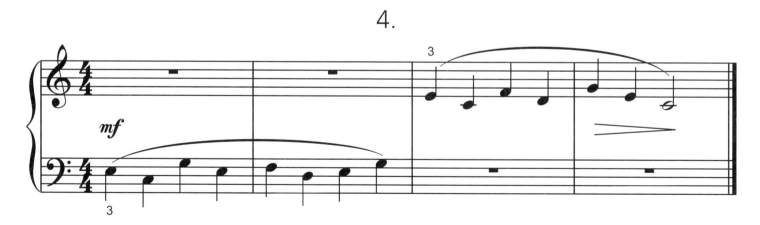

GP701

5.

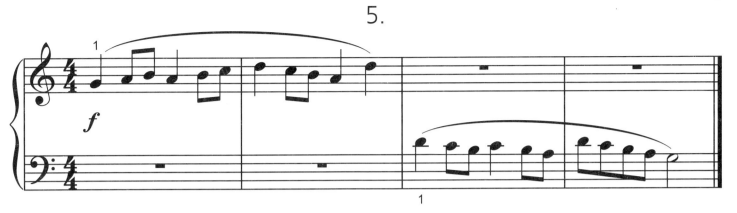

6.

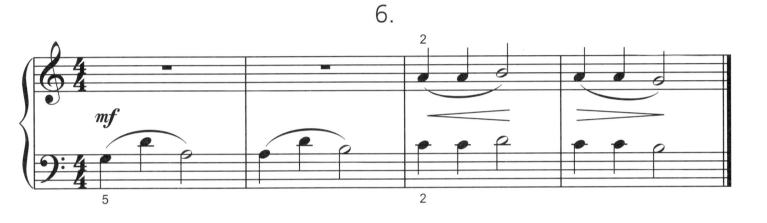

7.

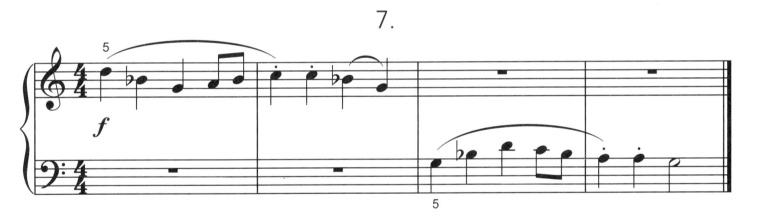

8.

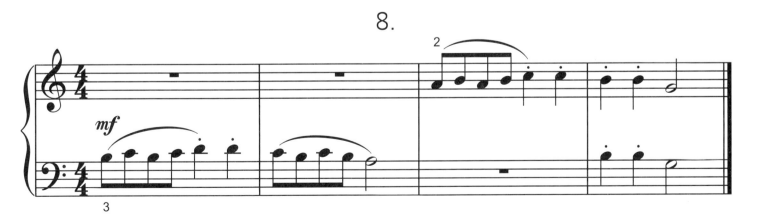

9.

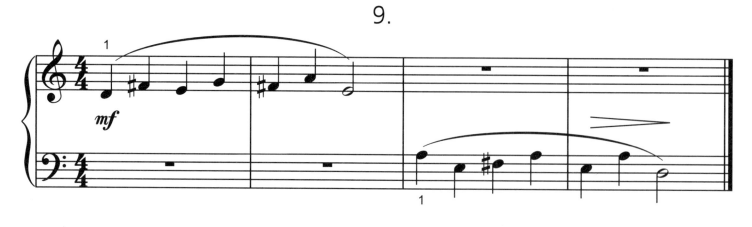

10.

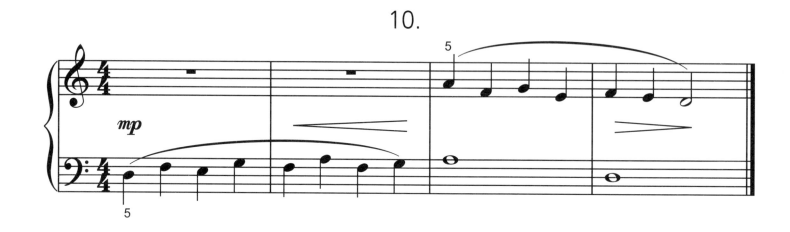

11.

12.

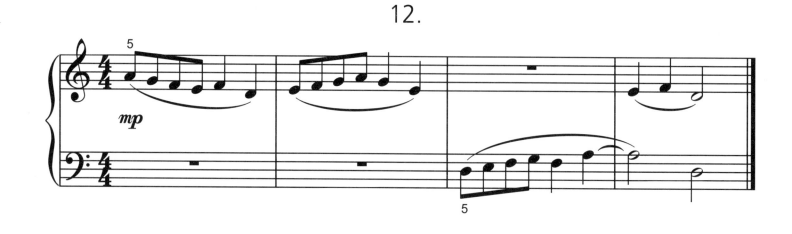

13.

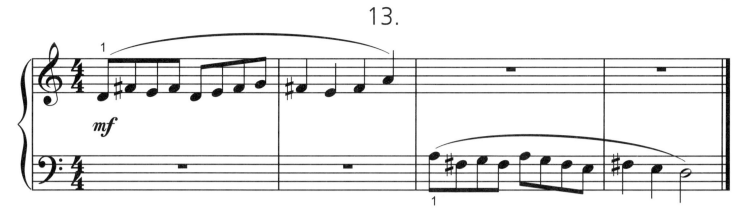

14.

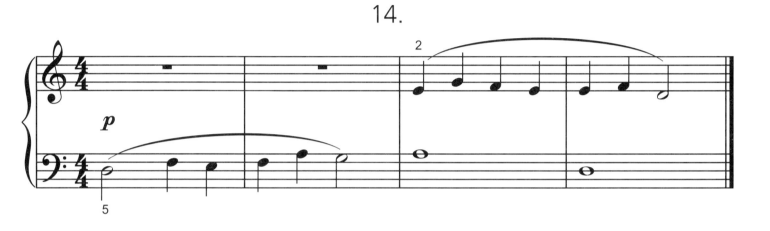

15.

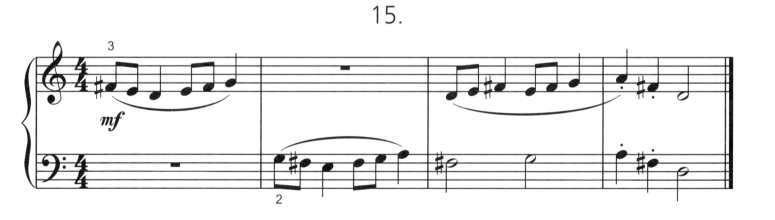

16.

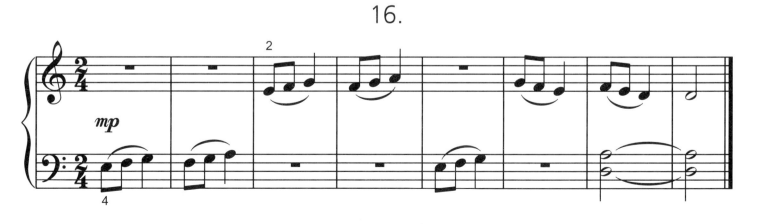

17.

18.

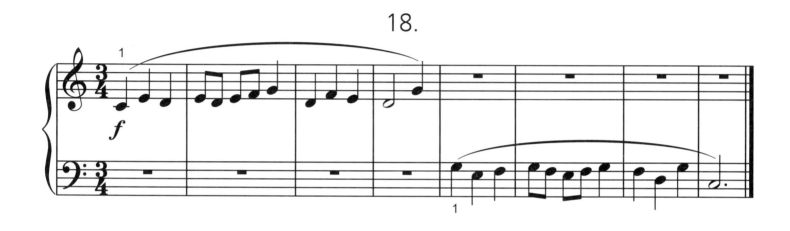

19.

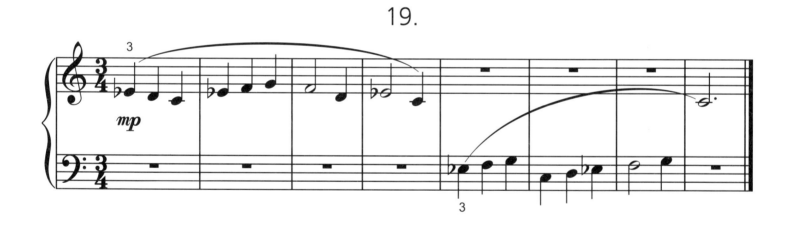

20.

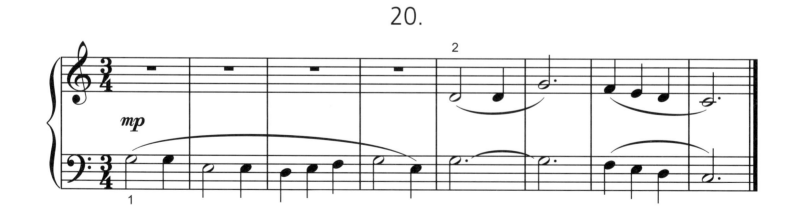

21.

22.

23.

24.

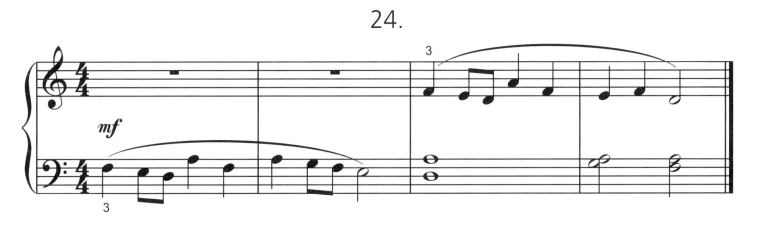

25.

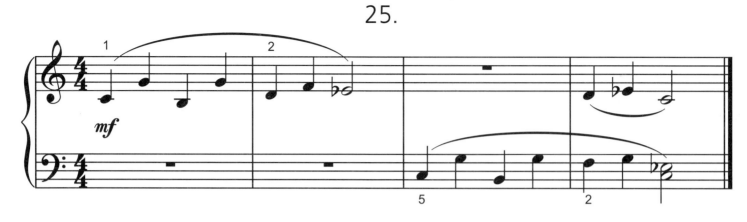

26.

27.

28.

29.

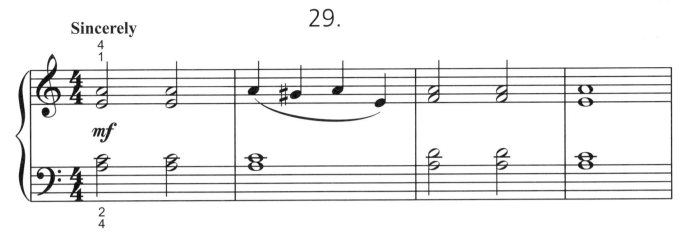

30.

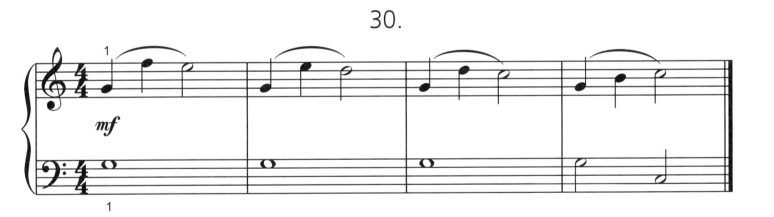

31.

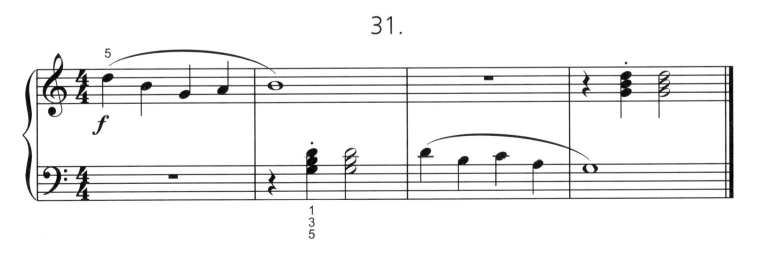

32.

33.

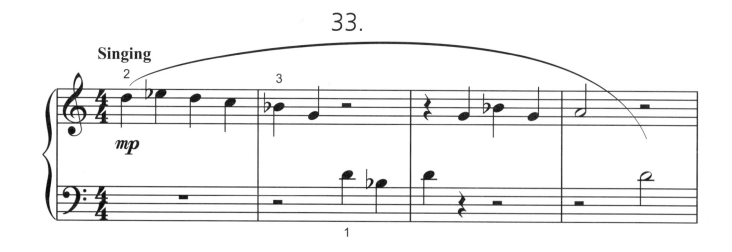

34.

35.

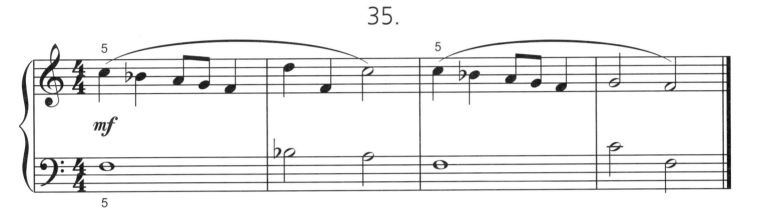

36.

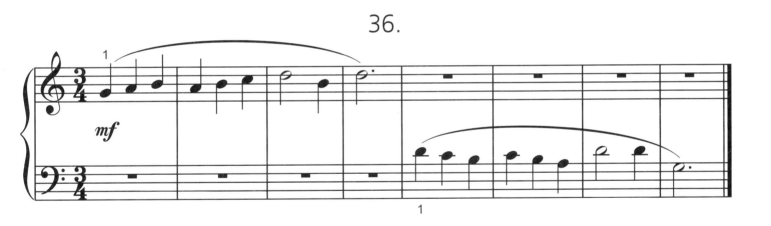

37.

38.

39.

40.

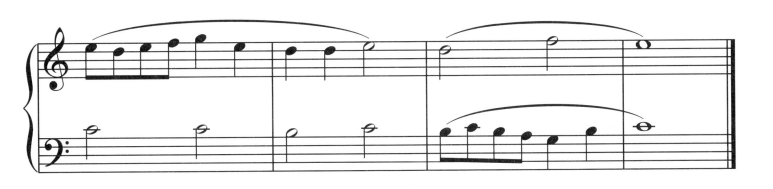

41.

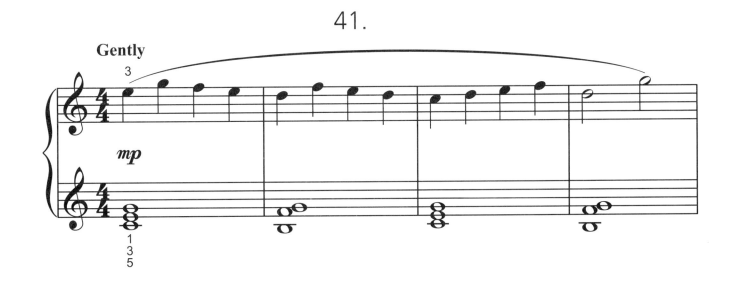

42.

Rhythmically

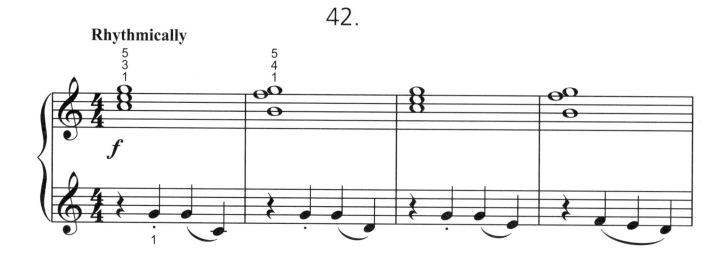

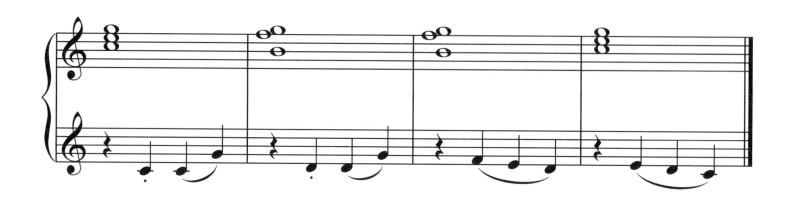

43.

Warmly

44.

45.

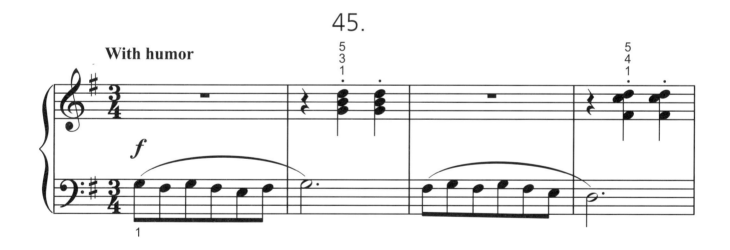

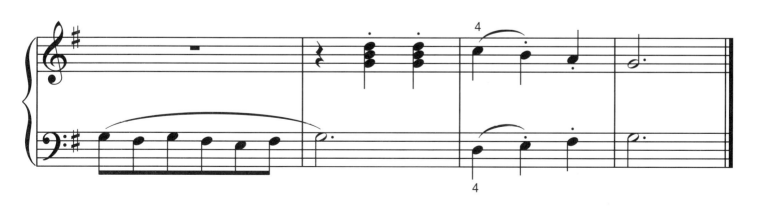

46.

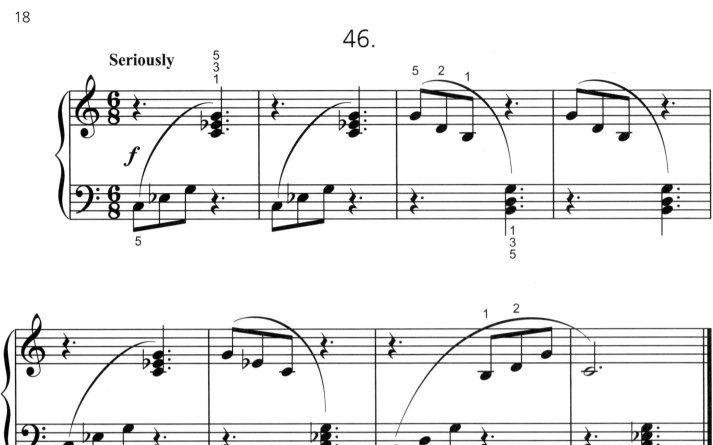

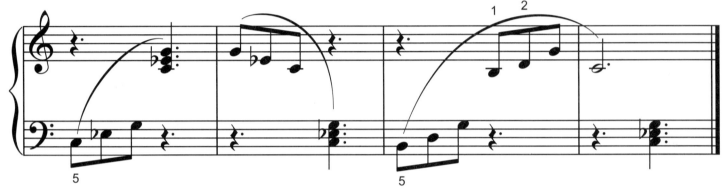

47.

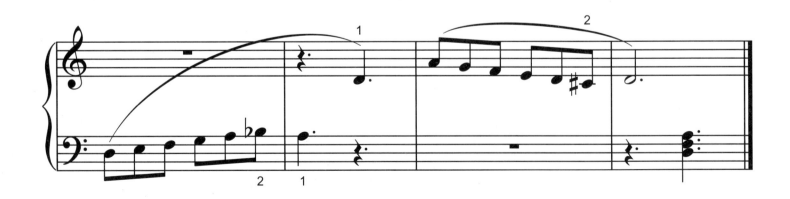

48.

49.

50.

51.

52.

53.

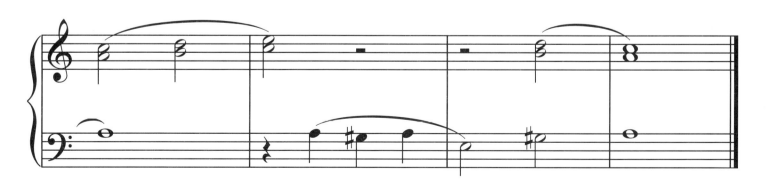

54.

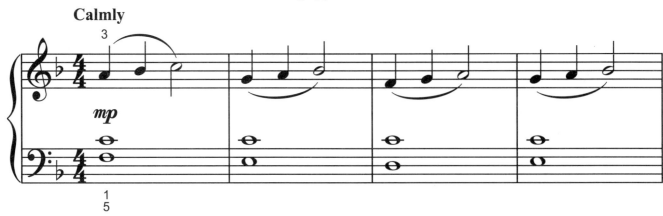

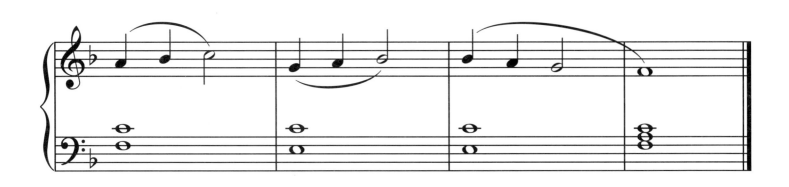

55.

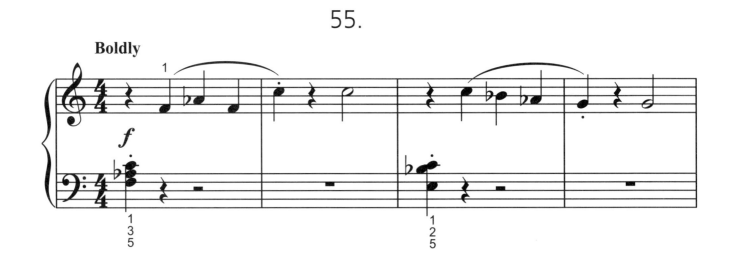

56.

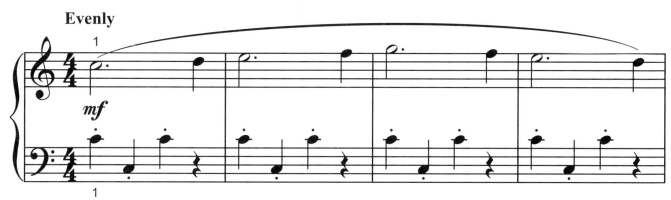

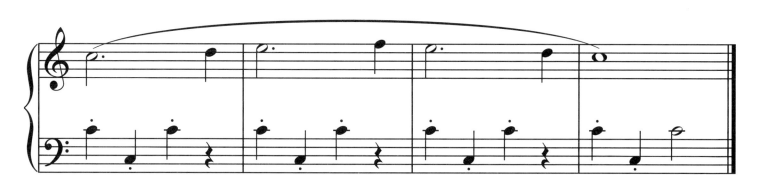

57.

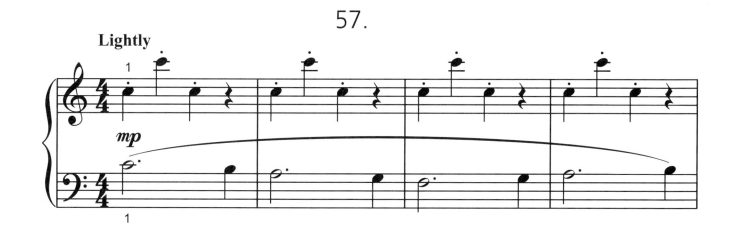

58.

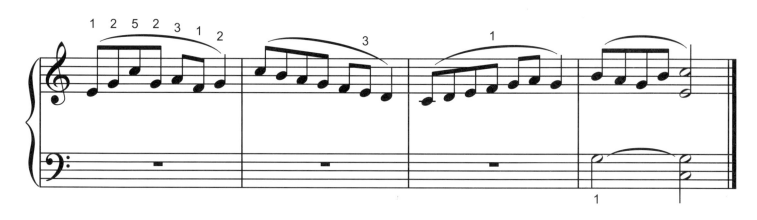

59.

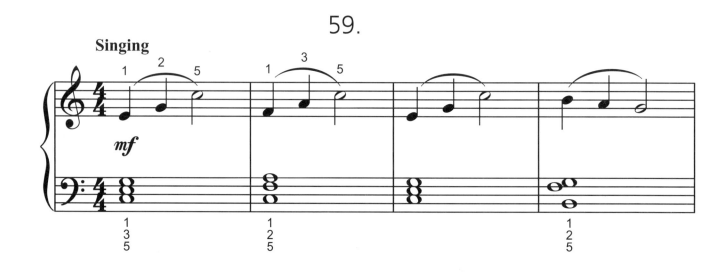

60.

61.

62.

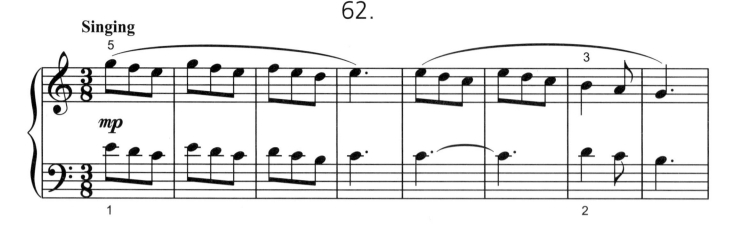

63.

64.

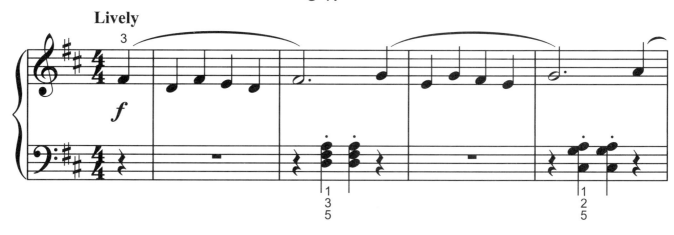

65.

66.

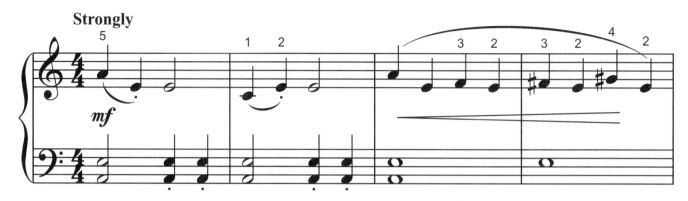

67.

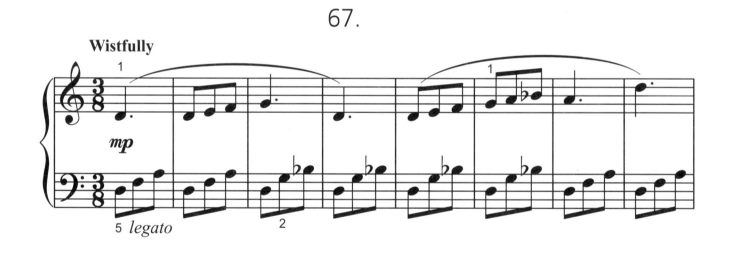

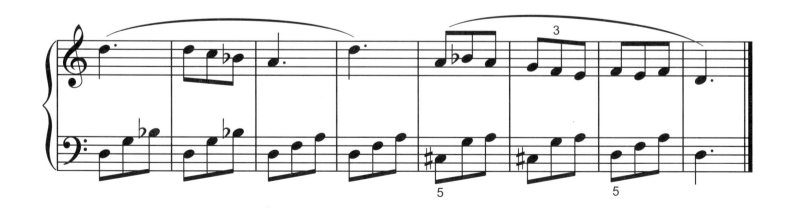

68.

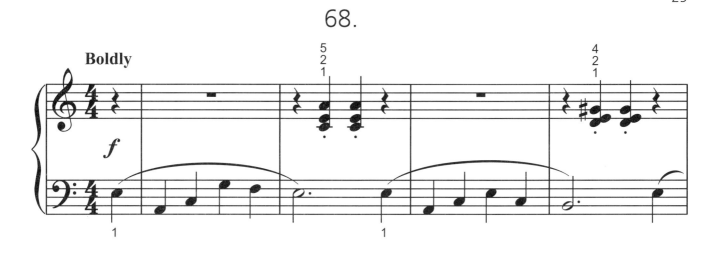

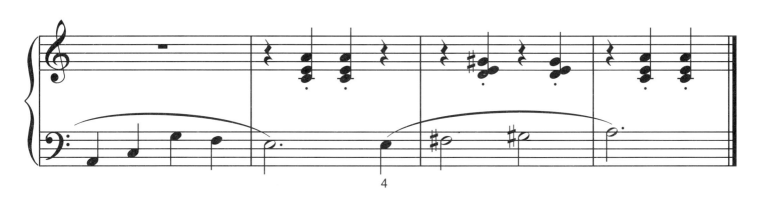

69.

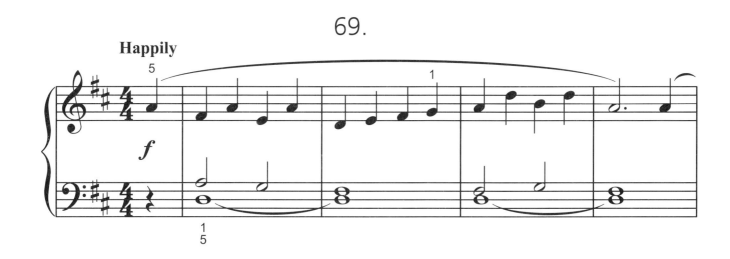

70.

71.

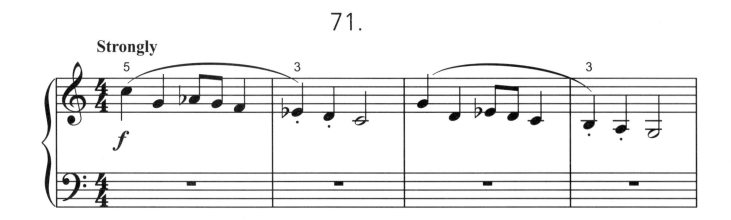

72.

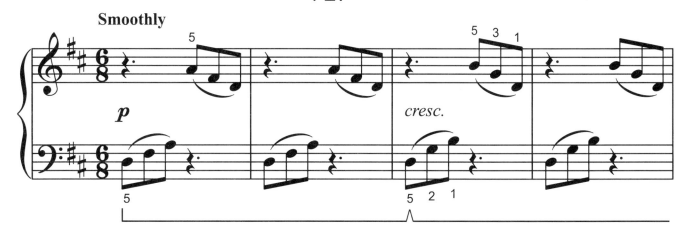

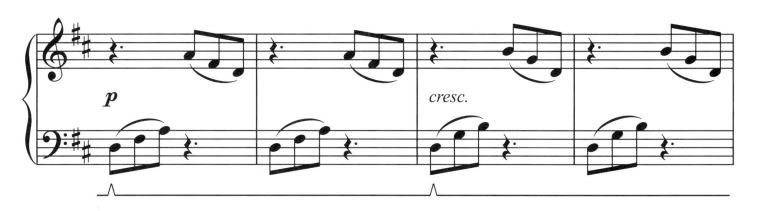